Bidding
on the Past

By

Jennifer Weinstein

Y0-ARC-006

Columbus, OH

Photos: 10, © Bettmann/Corbis; **17,** © Hulton Archive/Getty Images, Inc.; **29,** © Bettmann/Corbis.

Illustrations: Susan Lawson

SRAonline.com

Copyright © 2008 by SRA/McGraw-Hill.

All rights reserved. No part of this publication may be reproduced or distributed in any form or by any means, or stored in a database or retrieval system, without the prior written consent of The McGraw-Hill Companies, Inc., including, but not limited to, network storage or transmission, or broadcast for distance learning.

Send all inquiries to this address:
SRA/McGraw-Hill
4400 Easton Commons
Columbus, OH 43219

Printed in the United States of America.

ISBN: 978-0-07-611295-1
MHID: 0-07-611295-0

2 3 4 5 6 7 8 9 MAL 13 12 11 10 09 08

The **McGraw·Hill** Companies

Contents

— Chapter 1 —

Jazz Lives On

Regine stared through the window as the car traveled through the rain. She was with her Grandpa Russell. Soft jazz played on the radio. The *swish-swish* of the car's wipers kept time with the music. The sky was a deep gray. The weatherman on the television had been wrong. He had said it would be bright and sunny by noon. It was already 11:30 A.M., and the sun was nowhere in sight.

"That's okay," Regine thought. "It's better that it's raining. Now I don't feel so bad about having to go to this auction." Regine and her grandfather were heading into the city for an auction. The auction was to raise money for music education.

*"Jazz and blues," Regine said quietly.

"What was that, sweetheart?" Grandpa Russell asked.

"Nothing, Pops," Regine said. She liked spending time with her grandfather. But she wasn't really a fan of jazz or blues, his favorite kinds of music. She would much rather listen to rock or hip-hop. Jazz and blues were so boring.

"Pops, can't we listen to something else?" Regine asked. "This stuff all sounds the same."

Grandpa Russell smiled at her. "Do you know who this is? This is John Coltrane. He was one of the best saxophone players ever to play jazz."

Regine got ready for one of her grandfather's stories. She knew that once he got going, he could talk for hours. Grandpa Russell loved jazz and blues. When he was a young man, he* played in a jazz band. He also played the saxophone. He knew everything about the great jazz musicians like Coltrane.

"Coltrane," Grandpa Russell began, "was one of my biggest influences. I was 22 years old the first time I heard him play. He was playing with Miles Davis's band. I thought he was the best musician I had ever heard.

"I was a trumpet player at that time, you know. My dad had been a trumpet player too. He loved Louis Armstrong. He said Armstrong could blow a horn like nobody else. My dad used to spend hours trying to play like Armstrong. He . . ."

"Pops," Regine said, stopping him, "you were telling me about Coltrane."

"Oh, right, Coltrane," Grandpa Russell said, nodding. "I decided right then that I was going to play the saxophone, just like him. I listened to his music and saw him play every chance I got. In the 1960s he was looking for a new sound. So he used young musicians in his band. I always wished I could have played with him. His new sound, called 'hard bop,' was what got him noticed. Later he began experimenting. He brought in new instruments like African drums.

"He died young. It was a sad time for his fans. I took out my saxophone and played as many Coltrane songs as I could. Your mom was three then. She danced while I played. Then she came and sat on my lap. I told her about the times I had heard him play.

"I saw a television show about jazz a few weeks ago. Wynton Marsalis was on the show. He directs the Lincoln Center Jazz Orchestra. It's a highly respected job. On the show he said that Coltrane was *earnest*. That means he was serious and sharp. I think *earnest* is a good word to use about Coltrane. He was very serious about his art. He worked hard to play well. I admired that about him."

Grandpa Russell turned the car into a parking lot. "We're here," he said. "Let's go see some jazz and blues history."

— Chapter 2 —

Satchmo

They went into the lobby of the hotel where the auction was being held. Regine and Grandpa Russell were surprised at how many people were there. There were people of all races and ages. They were smiling and talking in small groups. Suddenly, the lights flashed. This let everyone know that the auction was about to begin. Regine and Grandpa Russell headed for the ballroom.

Inside the ballroom, Grandpa Russell led Regine to a pair of chairs near the front. Everybody seemed excited. Regine started to get interested.

"Pops, what kinds of things do you think they'll be selling?" she asked.

"From what I read, they'll be selling just about anything," Grandpa Russell answered. "I saw a list. There were evening gowns, musical instruments, albums, and books. After the normal auction, they'll have a silent auction. That's where they'll be selling the thing *I* want to buy. It's an album signed by Coltrane."

"Ladies and gentlemen please take your seats," a voice said from the front of the room.

*The crowd grew quiet as a tall man stepped to the microphone. "Good morning. We will begin the auction with items from the great jazz musicians. After a break, we will look at items from the great blues artists. Please remember that we are having this auction to help raise money for music education in our schools.

"The first item up for bid was given to us by the family of the late Louis Armstrong."

A pretty woman in a long blue dress brought out a shiny cornet.

"This cornet," the man told the crowd, "belonged to Armstrong. He was also known as 'Satchmo.' He was born in New Orleans in 1901 and died in 1971. The bidding will start at 10,000 dollars."

As people began shouting bids, Grandpa Russell* leaned over and whispered in Regine's ear. "I told you my father was a huge fan of Armstrong, remember? Let me tell you more about him—Armstrong, I mean, not my father.

Louis Armstrong plays a trumpet

"He learned to play cornet at a reform school when he was 12 years old. He got to be very good. He became the school's bandleader.

"After he left the school at age 14, Armstrong went home. He worked odd jobs to help his family. He worked on a junk wagon and delivered coal.

"He also played music on boats that went down the Mississippi River. As he grew older, Armstrong began playing in different bands and became very well known.

"He had a couple of nicknames. One was Satchmo. That was short for 'Satchel mouth' because of his large mouth. I know it sounds mean, but it was not supposed to be mean. Armstrong had a wide grin that made people smile with him. A lot of folks say that's where the name came from.

"People also called him 'Pops.' My father told me that Armstrong could never remember people's names, so he always called them 'Pops.' Except Pops Foster; Louis called him 'George.' " Grandpa Russell smiled. "I guess that's why folks started calling Armstrong 'Pops.' "

"Pops, that's what I call you," Regine pointed out.

"Yeah, your mom used to call my dad 'Pops' too. She must have heard him talking about Armstrong and liked the way it sounded. I like it when you call me 'Pops.' It makes me feel like I have something in common with old Satchmo." Grandpa Russell smiled at Regine.

"Armstrong traveled all over the world, bringing jazz to other countries. Did you know that jazz began in the United States? In fact, jazz music can be traced back to the time of slavery. African Americans would play music and sing for each other. They used handmade instruments and their voices to make different sounds. They often changed or made up the music as they played. That is called *improvisation*. Improvisation is a major part of jazz music.

"Armstrong was the first person ever to improvise a jazz solo. He did it back in the early 1900s. Many artists still copy the way he played. I'd bet that even some of the bands you listen to use his style."

Regine smiled. She thought of the bands she liked. She knew that many of them did use improvisation. Could the music she liked really have come from her grandfather's music?

Suddenly, the tall man at the front of the room banged the little hammer he was holding.

"Sold," he cried, "to the young man in the back!"

People began talking as they waited for the next item to bid on. Regine and Grandpa Russell sat quietly. They were both thinking about Satchmo and his place in music history.

— Chapter 3 —

The First Lady of Song

"The next item," the tall man began, "comes to us from the family of Ella Fitzgerald. She is known as the 'First Lady of Song.'"

The woman in the blue dress appeared again. This time she was carrying a beautiful silver gown.

The tall man went on, "This dress was worn by Fitzgerald when she sang in a show with Frank Sinatra. The bidding will start at 1,100 dollars."

Grandpa Russell whispered in Regine's ear again. "See Regine, jazz is more than just some guy blowing on a horn. The women of jazz were very popular and important as well.

Fitzgerald was one of the most popular female jazz singers ever. She opened doors for other African American artists."

"How did she do that?" Regine asked.

"Fitzgerald was young when she started out. She was about 15 or 16 years old. She dreamed of becoming a dancer, not a singer. It all started at the Apollo Theater in Harlem, a part of New York City. She signed up for a talent contest. At first she was going to dance, but she ended up singing instead.

"Now I've heard some folks say that Fitzgerald was a hit with the audience. I've also heard that she was booed off the stage.

Ella Fitzgerald sings for an audience

"It doesn't really matter now. People heard her and liked what they heard. She started singing with a band. It was one of the most popular jazz bands in New York.

*"The more Fitzgerald sang, the better she became. Thousands of people would come to hear the band play. People loved to dance to their music. They made up dances to go with the band's music. Some of the dances became popular all over the country."

"My friends and I learn a lot of dances from music videos," Regine said. "But how did Fitzgerald help African American musicians?"

Grandpa Russell smiled. "Fitzgerald was a great singer. She was one of the best improvisers in jazz. She could also make her voice sound like any instrument in the orchestra.

"She loved singing jazz and blues. She also wanted to sing ballads. A *ballad* is a long song that tells a story. At the time, the record companies didn't want African American artists* to sing ballads. But Fitzgerald sang them anyway and the door for other African Americans to sing ballads was opened.

"She also helped pave the way for female jazz singers. They were now able to tell stories through their songs. Nina Simone used her music to show a whole range of feelings. She wrote songs about the civil rights movement.

"Her songs were not played on the radio. But people sang them as they protested the way African Americans were being treated.

"Billie Holiday was another strong female jazz singer. Like Fitzgerald, Holiday had dreamed of becoming a dancer. She added something new to jazz singing. By singing more slowly, she gave jazz music a style closer to blues.

"Holiday also used her music to speak against racism. She had a soft but strong voice. Her powerful songs about African American life found a large audience."

"Who was your favorite, Pops?" Regine asked.

"Fitzgerald was my favorite," Grandpa Russell said. "Let me tell you more about her. After the leader of her band died, she took over for a couple of years. Then she went out on her own. She worked with other great jazz artists, like Armstrong.

"During her career she recorded over 2,000 songs. Her singing just kept getting better. People even recorded her live shows. Those recordings helped show what a fantastic scat singer she was. I'll have to play them for you sometime, Regine. You'll be stunned by the sounds that she could make with her voice.

"Many of the songs she sang were written by well-known songwriters. One of them was Ira Gershwin. He said he never knew how good his songs were until he heard Fitzgerald sing them."

"Did she ever win any awards?" Regine asked.

"Oh, yes," Grandpa Russell said. "She won just about every award there was to win. She won Grammys and the National Medal of Arts. She also won awards from other countries. She is even in the Grammy Hall of Fame."

"Pops, you said Fitzgerald did a lot of scat singing. What does that mean?" Regine asked.

"*Scat* is when a singer uses made-up words, or just syllables, while they sing," Grandpa Russell explained. "The story is that Armstrong started scat when he dropped the words to the song he was singing. He was recording at the time. So instead of stopping to pick up the words, he just made up sounds that went with the music, like *doo-da-li-bop*.

"I know you think jazz is boring, Regine. But the next time you're listening to rap or hip-hop music, think about what I've told you. I want you to think about where your music came from."

Grandpa Russell sat back in his chair. The bidding on Fitzgerald's evening gown came to an end. Regine watched him from the corner of her eye. She was still stunned that he could say jazz and hip-hop were alike.

She thought about the music she listened to on the radio. She also thought about what her grandfather had told her about jazz. Maybe her grandfather was right. But she still wasn't sure. She would have to ask him to tell her more.

Regine leaned over to her grandfather. "Pops, I'm tired of sitting," she said. "Let's go for a walk."

The two of them stood and made their way to the door.

— Chapter 4 —

Traps the Drum Wonder

Regine and Grandpa Russell wandered through the lobby of the hotel. On a far wall, Regine saw several black-and-white pictures.

"Let's look at those pictures," she said.

As they got closer to the pictures on the wall, Regine could see that they were of musicians. Under each picture were a name and a date.

"Louis Armstrong, 1924; Miles Davis and John Coltrane, 1955; Buddy Rich and Frank Sinatra, 1939," Regine read. She stopped in front of the third picture. "Who are they?" she asked her grandfather.

Grandpa Russell left the picture that he was looking at and went to stand by Regine.

"Wow, look how young they were. We were all that young once, I guess," he said with a sigh. "That is Buddy Rich and Frank Sinatra.

"The man on the left is Rich. He was a drummer. No, he wasn't just *a* drummer, he was *the* drummer. Gene Krupa once said there are great drummers, and then there's Buddy Rich.

"Before Rich started in jazz, the best drummer around was Krupa. I remember hearing an interview with Rich and Krupa on the radio once.

*"Krupa said he had been afraid to hear Rich play, because he had heard Rich was so good.

"As I recall, Rich started playing drums when he was just a baby. His mother and father were in vaudeville. Vaudeville shows had short acts like comedy, singing, and dancing. It was a popular form of entertainment in the early 1900s. They put Rich on stage when he was only 18 months old. He was called 'Traps the Drum Wonder.'

"Even at that young age, Rich was a gifted drummer. He never had a lesson and said he never practiced. He only played during shows. Somehow, he just knew how to play.

"As a child, Rich was a star in many vaudeville shows. He was a pretty good singer and tap dancer,* but drumming was where he made his mark.

"Rich played fast, loud, and hard. But he also played with great care. For a few years, he played in some of the most popular bands in the country. But he really made a name for himself when he started his own band.

"He did something no drummer had ever done before. He tuned his drums so he could play melodies on them. Now modern drummers copy this style. I saw a CD at the store called *A Tribute to Buddy Rich*. Some of today's best drummers got together and played Rich's music.

"I think what people liked most about Rich was his emotion when he played. Everybody could feel his music. When he played, you just had to listen.

Buddy Rich at his drum set

"He was so good that he even played for some of our presidents. He also played for kings and queens all over the world.

"Because of his creative drumming style, Rich stayed popular even as rock and roll took over. A lot of today's drummers look up to him. His jazz style works well for rock. A modern drummer once said that if you can play jazz, you can play anything. That's because jazz is the hardest thing to play."

Regine noticed that the lobby of the hotel was filling with people. "Sorry, Pops," she said to her grandfather. "It looks like we missed the jazz auction."

"It's okay, sweetheart," Grandpa Russell answered. "We can go back in for the blues auction. But first, let's get some lunch."

Chapter 5

Father of Rock and Roll

Regine and Grandpa Russell finished their lunch. As they were walking back to the hotel lobby, the lights flashed again.

"Looks like it's time to get back to the auction," Regine said.

They followed the mass of people back to the ballroom. The tall man was already at the microphone. He waited for the crowd to quiet down before speaking.

"Good afternoon. Welcome to the second half of our auction. We will now be seeing items from the great blues artists. Let us begin with the first item. It is from the family of Robert Johnson."

The woman in the blue dress was gone. This time a woman in a pink suit brought out a shiny guitar.

The tall man told the crowd, "Johnson only recorded 29 songs, but was said to have shaped modern music. The bidding on his guitar will start at 10,000 dollars."

Regine realized she was waiting for the man to finish talking so Grandpa Russell could tell her more about this artist. She looked at him and saw a smile on his face. She could tell he had a story for her. She leaned in closer to hear him whisper.

*"Much of the music you listen to can be traced back to blues, Regine. Jazz, rock and roll, hip-hop, and rap all came from blues. And blues was born from slavery.

"Blues was more than a style of music. It was a way of life. It was a way for African Americans to share their day-to-day lives. Slaves used to sing to keep in touch with one another when they were working in the fields. After slavery ended, African Americans made their music sound like that singing. Only instead of answering another person, the singer would answer himself or herself. Or a guitar would answer the singer. W. C. Handy was known as the 'Father of the Blues.' He was the first person to write a song with *blues* in* the title.

"Johnson was born in the birthplace of blues—Mississippi," Grandpa Russell said. "He was a great guitar player. But he didn't start out that way.

"When Johnson first started playing guitar, the other men he played with made fun of him for his lack of skill. After a short time Johnson left them. He returned to his home in Mississippi and spent several months practicing and writing songs. When he returned, he was better than any other guitar player.

"Now Johnson is seen as one of the people who helped shape modern music. He was only 27 when he died. He didn't have time to become as popular as some other artists. But among rock musicians, Johnson is known as one of the fathers of rock and roll.

"One of the things that made Johnson so great was his songwriting. Lots of bands have played songs he wrote. The Rolling Stones even recorded some of his music.

In fact, Keith Richards, who is one of The Rolling Stones's guitarists, said that the first time he heard Johnson, he thought he was hearing two guitars. That's how good Johnson was. He could do things with a guitar that nobody else could."

Regine was about to ask her grandfather what songs Johnson had written when the tall man banged the little hammer again. The sound startled her, and she forgot her question.

— Chapter 6 —

A Special Guest

"Ladies and gentlemen," the tall man said, "we have a special guest with us today. Please join me in welcoming the great blues guitarist B. B. King."

The audience went wild. People clapped and whistled.

An older man near the podium stood and waved to the audience. The tall man waited a moment for the clapping to stop. Then he spoke.

"Thank you so much for welcoming him so warmly," he said. "The items in this auction come from the best artists this country has seen. Mr. King is hoping that the money we raise today will help more children learn to love music the way he does. As a special treat, Mr. King will play a few songs for all of us at the end of this auction."

King waved to the audience again and sat down. The audience stood and clapped loudly until the tall man calmed them down.

"The next artist is Bessie Smith," he said. "Her family has been kind enough to give us one of her albums."

The woman in the pink suit came out with a record album.

"Like many early blues musicians," he went on, "Smith was born to a poor family. Her parents died when she was young. To get by, she and her brother would sing on the streets for pennies.

"When she got older, she became part of a show as a dancer and singer. Smith had a strong singing voice. She was popular all over the country. But she was really loved in the South.

"Smith came a long way from singing on the streets for pennies. In the 1920s, she was the highest-paid African American entertainer in the country.

"She worked with some of the best jazz musicians, like Armstrong and Benny Goodman. She influenced them as much as they influenced her. Both male and female blues singers worked to sing like her.

"Smith made the first electronically recorded album. A copy of this album, *Cake Walking Babies,* has been given to us for this event. Ladies and gentlemen, the bidding will start at 1,000 dollars."

The shouting of bids began. Grandpa Russell turned to Regine.

"They should have the items for the silent auction ready," he said. "Let's go take a look."

The two made their way out of the crowded ballroom and into the lobby. A man wearing glasses was at the front desk. He showed them where the silent auction items were.

Grandpa Russell and Regine went into a smaller ballroom. Tables were set up around the room. Several items were on each table. Next to each item sat a card, a box, a pen, and a pad of paper.

"The card tells you what the item is and who owned it," Grandpa Russell explained. "The pad of paper is where you write your bid."

Regine spotted a beautiful necklace on one of the tables. She walked over to read its card. "Pearl Necklace—Gertrude 'Ma' Rainey," it read.

Looking over Regine's shoulder, Grandpa Russell read the card. "Ma Rainey. Yes, the 'Mother of the Blues,' " he said.

Regine turned around and asked, "Who was she?"

"Rainey was the first woman to sing the blues," Grandpa Russell explained. "She and her husband traveled all over, singing and dancing together. She had a powerful voice and was well known in the South. It wasn't until her first song was recorded that the rest of the country got to know her. That first recording was made 25 years after she started singing the blues.

"Remember Smith? Well, she worked with Rainey in a traveling show. The two women became friends. Many people believe that Rainey coached Smith in her singing. I understand Rainey was a good businesswoman too," he said. "She owned two theaters and was able to retire when blues began to lose its popularity."

*Grandpa Russell turned away from the necklace and wandered around the room. Regine followed him, asking about the artists as they passed each item.

Suddenly, Grandpa Russell stopped. Regine was looking at a picture on a table while she walked, and she ran right into his back.

"This is it," Grandpa Russell whispered.

Regine looked at the table. There was an old record album on the tablecloth. Next to the album a card read, "Signed Album—John Coltrane."

Regine watched as her grandfather gently touched the album cover. Then he slowly picked up the pad of paper. He took the pen off the table and wrote something on the paper. Then he put the piece of paper in the box on the table.

"Let's go home, Regine," he said.

On* the way home, Regine listened to jazz music with new ears.

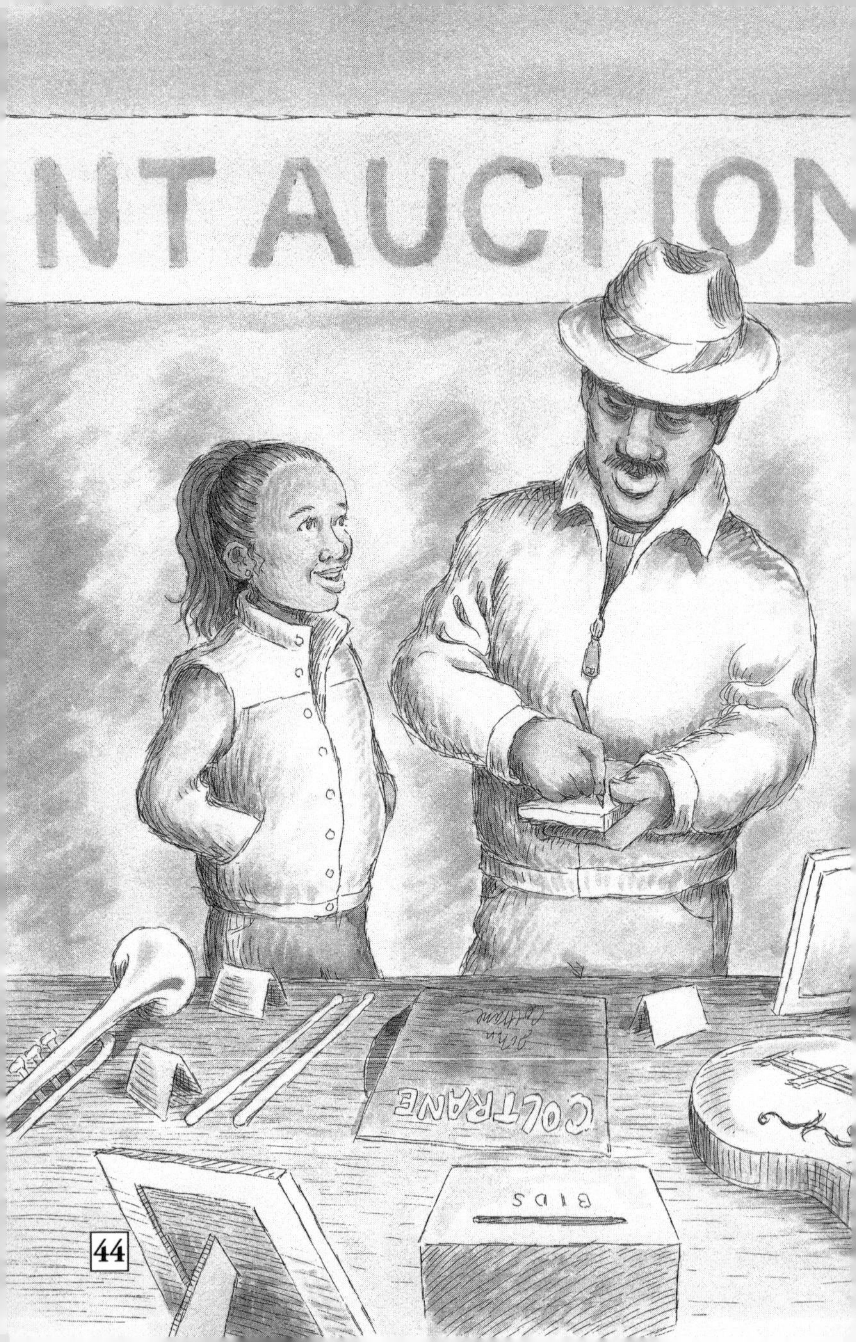
NT AUCTION
COLTRANE
BIDS